D1135039

Beyblade
Vol. 1

Story and Art by Takao Aoki

English Adaptation/Fred Burke
Translation/Akira Watanabe
Touch-up Art & Lettering/Dave Lanphear
Cover Design/Carolina Ugalde
Interior Design/Sean Lee
Editor/Ian Robertson

Managing Editor/Annette Roman
Director of Production/Noboru Watanabe
Editorial Director/Alvin Lu
Sr. Director of Licensing & Acquisitions/Rika Inouye
Vice President of Marketing/Liza Coppola
Vice President of Sales/Joe Morici
Executive Vice President/Hyoe Narita
Publisher/Seiji Horibuchi

Published by VIZ, LLC
P.O. Box 77010
San Francisco, CA 94107

10 9 8 7 6 5 4 3 2 1
First printing, September 2004

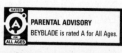

PARENTAL ADVISORY
BEYBLADE is rated A for All Ages.

store.viz.com

www.viz.com

Contents

Story and Art by

Takao Aoki

8

FROM NOW ON JUST CALL ME BEYBLADE KING!

THAT TYSON GUY'S REALLY GOOD.

MAYBE *TOO* GOOD! HAS HE EVER *LOST*?

HUH!

TIKKA TEKK.

I'LL JOT THAT DOWN!

"TYSON. PERSONALITY: *EGOCENTRIC*. ABILITY: *AVERAGE*."

WHAT DO *I* KNOW? JUST ABOUT *EVERYTHING*! BEYBLADES ARE THE SUBJECT OF MY RESEARCH!

WHO ARE *YOU* TO DIS *ME*, HUH, CHIEF? WHADDA *YOU* KNOW ABOUT BEYBLADES!?

HERE YA GO, MASARU! IT'S LUCKY YOUR PRIZED BEYBLADE DIDN'T GET BROKEN.

YOU SURE DID!

OUCH! BUT I GOT IT...

GOOD OL' TYSON.

THANKS, TYSON. I OWE YOU ONE...

Y-YEAH! VERY LUCKY!

MY BEYBLADE GOT TAKEN!

GEE, KENTA! WHAT'S UP!?

HE CO QU YO GU

GIVE IT BACK TO HIM!

THAT'S MINE!

HEY! THIS ONE'S *MINE* NOW, BUB! THE SPOILS OF WAR! *HEH...*

TWMP

USE IT OR LOSE IT! *THAT'S* THE RULE OF THE BLADE SHARKS!

OH, YEAH? WHO SAYS, TOUGH GUY?

NO ONE' TAKING A BEYBLAD AROUND *HERE!*

THE BLADE SHARKS!?

I'VE HEARD OF THEM! A GANG OF BEYBLADE BULLIES WHO'LL STOP AT *NOTHING* TO GET THEIR WAY!

THEIR TACTICS ARE THE *WORST!*

I WON'T LET YOU GET AWAY WITH IT!

Fwoosh

TYSON!

GUESS WE SHOULD JUST GIVE UP OUR 'BLADES *NOW...*

SO MUCH FOR US, HUH?

THE ONLY *WIMP* HERE IS *YOU!*

OKAY! WHO'S UP NEXT? OR HAVE YOUR SPINES ALL GONE LIMP, WIMPS!?

yikes

yikes

BLADE SHARKS

VSH

LET IT RIP!

VSH

ZANG

KCHANG

KNOCK
HIM OUT
OF THE
RING!

WHAT!?

heh

C'MON!
PUSH
HIM
OUT!

TYSON'S
BEYBLADE
IS ON THE
OFFENSIVE!
ALL *RIGHT!*

VWOSH

KRNCH

GOTTA GET MY BEY-BLADE!

WHOOSH!

I'LL FIGHT YOU ANY TIME!

IF YOU'RE SO UPSET, YOU CAN ALWAYS BATTLE FOR IT!

I'LL TAKE THAT, LOSER!

AFTER ALL, HOW OFTEN DO I GET TO BEAT THE PANTS OFF *ROYALTY?* SEE YA LATER, *KING!*

HA HA HA

YOU JERK! GIVE IT BACK!

VIWEE

KNSH

HEY! WAIT UP! WHO ARE YOU!?

ZEEOOSH

WHAT A COOL BEYBLADE!

YOU OKAY? HEY!

ARE YOU ALL RIGHT, TYSON!?

THAT GUY *GAVE* THIS TO ME!?

TYSON!

I HATE TO ADMIT IT... BUT THAT GUY'S RIGHT!

HUH!? THERE'S A BLUE DRAGON CARVED IN THE CENTER.

...WHEN I LOOK AT THIS DRAGOON, I FEEL *POWER* RISE UP INSIDE OF ME!

I'M *FINE!* IT'S JUST *ODD*...

WHAT'S WRONG, TYSON!?

GNN

LET'S GO, DRAGOON!

WE'RE GONNA TAKE CARE OF THAT BULLY ONCE AND FOR ALL!

SKRRSH!

I'M GOING TO NAME THIS ONE *DRAGOON*, DUDE!

THEN WE JUST HAVE TO INCREASE THE TORQUE AND USE A RAPID ATTACK STRATEGY!

THAT'S WHY I PLANNED AHEAD! CHECK IT OUT!

CHAAK

SEE?! IT'S SPINNING A LOT FASTER THAN BEFORE!

VWRRSH

LET IT RIP!

SKRRR

LONG LIVE THE KING!

I PUT TWO SHOOTER RACKS END TO END!

SHOOTER

SHOOTER RACK

SO IT'S NOT ENOUGH, HUH? HOW MUCH DO WE NEED TO INCREASE IT BY!?

BUT IT'S STILL ONLY TWICE THE TORQUE THAT IT WAS BEFORE.

GET OFF MY CASE, WILL YA!

YOU REALLY PUT THAT LITTLE BRAIN TO USE!

FOUR TIMES MORE!? BUT *HOW...*?

LEMME SEE... BY **FOUR TIMES!** THAT WOULD BEAT HIM!

STILL FULL OF THE OLD CHILDISH ENTHUSIASM, TYSON!

THAT'S *NOT* WHAT I'M SAYING...

THERE'S NO WAY! I CAN'T MAKE THE SHOOTER RACK ANY LONGER!

MY ARM'S TOO SHORT!

I'M COUNTING ON YOU, DRAGOON! A LOT'S AT STAKE!

IT'S UP TO US!

PLEASE, I DON'T WANNA GET MY BEYBLADE TAKEN...!

POOM

POOM

LET IT RIP!

ZZEE

44

ALL RIGHT! WAY TO GO, DRAGOON! THAT WAS PERFECT!

GRANDPA!

SO *THAT'S* WHAT YOU'VE BEEN UP TO!

LET'S WIN TODAY'S BATTLE THE SAME WAY!

WAAAH!

I DON'T CARE *WHAT* IT IS! SWORD PRACTICE! 1000 SWINGS! *BEGIN!*

THEY'RE NOT TOPS, THEY'RE BEY-BLADES!

SWORDS-MANSHIP DEMANDS PRACTICE! PLAYING WITH *TOPS* IS FOR--

49

WHY'D YOU DO THAT, TYSON!?

I HAD TO!

WHAT!?

WRAK

VSH

WELL, I'LL BE!

THAT'S RIGHT. AND I ALMOST STEPPED ON THEM...

THESE FLOWERS! BEFORE SHE DIED, MOM LOVED THEM.

WHAT AMAZING STRENGTH THAT TYSON HAS!

WHA?! MY SWORD! BROKEN IN TWO!

CARLOS IS THE WINNER FROM THE A BLOCK!

HE'S ALSO REIGNING CHAMPION OF LAST YEAR'S FIERCE TOURNAMENT!

WE LOOK FORWARD TO THESE TWO DOING BATTLE IN JUST THIRTY MINUTES!

WOW! YAY!

THAT HITS THE SPOT!

ALL I GOTTA DO IS STAY RELAXED FOR THE FINALS...

gulp gulp gulp

YOU CAN SAY THAT!

WHAT'S UP, CHIEF! ARE YOU HERE TO DO MORE RESEARCH?

SORRY IF I'M COCKY!

WHOA! EVEN ONE AS COCKY AS YOU CAN GET NERVOUS, HUH!?

I'D LIKE TO ASK YOU THE SAME THING!

HEY! WHAT'S THE BIG IDEA!? OWW!

IF YOU'RE A BEYBLADER, YOU SHOULD KNOW HOW PRECIOUS THESE ARE!

...IS NO MORE THAN A *TOOL!*

TO THE *BLADE SHARKS,* A BEYBLADE ...

GRRRR

YOUR NAME'S TYSON, HUH? YOU'LL REGRET THIS!

Blade Shark FWAP

SO HE'S ONE OF THEM!

THE MOST FEARED BULLIES OF THE BEYBLADE WORLD!

BLADE SHARKS!

HUH!?

I'M SCARED. IS THERE STILL TIME TO APOLOGIZE?

PSS PSS

HE'S A BLADE SHARK, HUH?

WHAT!?

YOU'RE ANNOYING! I DON'T LIKE YOUR ATTITUDE, KID!

WMP

SHUCKIES, SHARKIES, **WHO CARES?!** HE'S THE ONE WHO SHOULD APOLOGIZE!

UH, *BLADE* SHARKS.

THE FINAL WILL BE THREE MATCHES IN A ROW!

ALL DATA THUS FAR SHOWS THAT...

...CARLOS USES THE *DIRTIEST* TACTICS POSSIBLE-- SO BE EXTREMELY CAREFUL!

SO TWO OUT OF THREE IS THE *CHAMP!*

HERE IT IS... FACE-OFF!

I'LL PLAY FAIR AND GIVE IT MY BEST SHOT!

WILL DO! THANKS, CHIEF!

WHAT A GUY...

64

DON'T END THE MATCH YET...

NO! WAIT A SEC!

YAAA!

FINE! THEN IT'S OVER! YOU...

YAAA!

aaah

IS HE FOR *REAL?*

LET US FIGHT TO THE END!

...IT'S A *SERIOUS* BATTLE BETWEEN CARLOS AND ME!

YAAA!

DO IT, TYSON!

WAY TO GO!

OKAY THEN! IT'S YOUR CALL!

DAMN THIS GOODY-GOODY! I'LL SHOW HIM!

MY HAND... I CAN BARELY GRIP THE SHOOTER.

OW!

OW!

...BUT, I CAN'T LET THIS...

BUT...

WUM

WUM

HOLD ME BACK!

BEGIN THE SECOND BATTLE. SHOOT!

THE CHIEF MAY BE RIGHT. MY...

OW...

LET'S RESIGN. YOU DID ALL YOU COULD.

HOW CAN I BATTLE LIKE THIS!?

...MY HAND... STARTING TO GO NUMB.

I NEED MY FULL STRENGTH AT A TIME LIKE THIS!

DON'T RELY ON YOUR SURFACE STRENGTH, TYSON!

TYSON!

TYSON!

YOU CAN DO IT!

GO FOR IT!

BUT ALL THE KIDS...

CHAPTER 2: NEVER GIVE UP!

HE CAUGHT ME OFF GUARD, THAT'S ALL!

I'LL SHOW HIM NEXT TIME!

NAH, LET ME!

I'LL GET HIM!

KAI, LET ME DO THE HONORS! PLEASE?

NO. IT IS OUR TURN NEXT.

HUH!?

TNCH

TYSON WON'T STAND A CHANCE AGAINST THE BLADE SHARK FOUR!

C'MON! LET US HAVE HIM!

HMPH! DON'T EVEN TRY IT!

...AND IT'S A SECRET OF GREAT POWER, THAT'S FOR SURE!

I CAN FEEL IT...

THAT BEYBLADE OF YOURS HAS SOME KIND OF *SECRET* HIDDEN WITHIN IT!

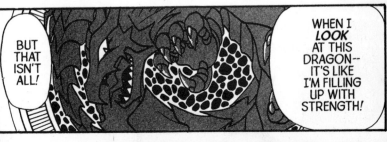

BUT THAT ISN'T ALL!

WHEN I *LOOK* AT THIS DRAGON-- IT'S LIKE I'M FILLING UP WITH STRENGTH!

I'VE BEEN WITH THIS DRAGON *BEFORE!* I KNOW IT!

WE'VE KNOWN EACH OTHER FOR A LONG, LONG TIME!

... I JUST CAN'T HOLD BACK MY SCIENTIFIC CURIOSITY ANY LONGER!

...HOW HE MUST FEEL... AND YET I...

I KNOW HOW HE...

HEY, CHIEF! WAIT!

...BUT I *MUST* FIND OUT MORE!

TYSON, I PROMISE NOT TO DAMAGE IT IN ANY WAY...

WSH

WHAT IS IT WITH THAT GUY? DOES KAI ACTUALLY THINK WE'D *LOSE* AGAINST TYSON!?

THAT MAKES ME MAD!

TRASH

BAM

YEAH! WE DID IT!

OOSH!

THE WAY THAT BEYBLADE WAS MOVING...

...IT WAS LIKE THE DRAGOON COULD READ TYSON'S MIND!

WHAT DO YOU MEAN... "AT TIMES"?

THAT RESEARCH OF YOURS COMES IN HANDY AT TIMES, CHIEF!

AND WHAT IS A DYNA-LOOP?

fip

fap

VSH

TSH

I CAN'T BELIEVE IT! THE BLADE SHARK FOUR... BEATEN.

CHAPTER 3: LEGENDARY!

TINK

I THINK NOT, KAI! FOR SUCH DECISIONS ARE NOT UP TO *YOU!*

YOU SEE HOW IT GOES? *NOW* IT'S *MINE!*

DON'T TOUCH THAT, KAI!

VWRR

I WANTED TO TAKE IT WITH NO DAMAGE, BUT...

...THE POWER WILL BE MINE-- EVEN IF I MUST DESTROY THE BLADE!

IF IT'S A FAIR FIGHT, I'M IN!

HEH, HEH, HEH!

LET'S DO IT!

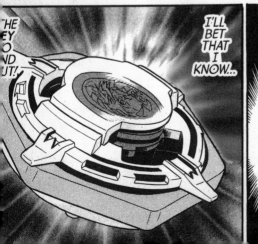

THE EY O ND UT!

I'LL BET THAT I KNOW...

HE CAME TO MAKE THE TWO OF THEM BATTLE EACH OTHER!

JUST WHO IS THIS JIN GUY!?

WSH

TYSON!

PWUP

DOES KAI BATTLE *JUST* TO DESTROY BEYBLADES!?

IT'S AN OUTRAGE!

...I'LL WIN AT *ANY* COST!

I CAN'T LOSE TO KAI! I...

GWMM

LET ME SEE YOUR *TRUE* SKILL!

SKRRR

THIS WILL BE A THREE ROUND FIGHT!

THE FIRST ROUND IS *NOW!*

ET IT RIP!

YAA!

ALL RIGHT! THE SPEED AND TORQUE ARE RIGHT ON POINT!

DRAGOON! GO FOR IT!

POOR KAI IS STUCK IN THE MIDDLE!

FOOL! I KNEW HOW YOU WOULD ATTACK FROM THE VERY START!

I'LL USE MY FAVORITE ATTACK AND BOOT HIM OUT OF THE RING!

WHAT, TYSON? WHAT?!

AHHH!

ONE POINT TO KAI... THE DRAGOON FLIPPED OVER!

OH, NO!

SKRK

RK

THE DRAGOON IT'S GOT A...A *CRACK!*

KAI JUST WANTED TO SEE WHAT TYSON WAS CAPABLE OF! WE'VE BEEN TRICKED!

KAI?! WHAT DO YOU MEAN, HIRUTA?

DAMN THAT KAI ANY-HOW...

WE'RE NOTHING BUT **TOOLS** FOR KAI... JUST LIKE THE BEYBLADES!

ARE YOU SAYING KAI USED US... ...RIGHT FROM SQUARE ONE!?

...I'M **SCARED** OF KAI!

THIS **FEAR!** I...

RMB RMB RMB RMB

IT'S TRUE THAT TYSON HASN'T BEEN ABLE TO BRING OUT EVEN **HALF** OF THE DRAGOON'S POWERS...

...AND YET...

YOU CAN'T EVEN LIVE UP TO YOUR WORDS!

TSH

I GUESS YOU OVER-ESTIMATED TYSON'S SKILLS, EH, JIN!

THE RAIN! THAT'S *IT!*

OUCH...I SLIPPED IN THIS *PUDDLE!*

HUH*!?*

OKAY! IT'S TIME FOR...

...OUR ROUND *TWO!* PLACES PLEASE!

SHAAA

HE'LL *NEVER* QUIT!

GO FOR THE WIN!

DRAGOON, JUST KEEP IT UP! YEAH!

NOW THE LEGENDARY BEYBLADES WILL SHOW THEIR TRUE POWERS AT LAST!

THE TIME HAS COME!

WH... WHAT'S GOING ON HERE!?

142

SXRR

DRAGOON!?

TMSH

TYSON!?

ALL *RIGHT!* YOU WON, TYSON!

DRANZER!

SHAA

KAI... HE LOST-- FOR THE FIRST TIME!

AND TO A PIPSQUEAK LIKE THAT! WHO'D'A THUNK IT?!

...THE BLUE DRAGON POWER!

YOUR BACK WAS TO THE WALL, TYSON! BUT YOU FINALLY CALLED FORTH...

DRAGOON!

RRNK!

I'LL PUT YOU BACK TOGETHER! YOU'LL SEE!

OH, NO! DRA...

TSH

WSH

HAVE TO TAKE A RAINCHECK. DRANZER'S NOT IN ANY SHAPE TO DO BATTLE EITHER.

TIED, ONE TO ONE BUT DRAGOON IS IN BAD SHAPE!

IT'S YOUR VICTORY, KAI--BY DEFAULT. SO...

Heh, heh, heh!

FINE! WE'LL CONTINUE ROUND THREE IN A NEW TIME AND PLACE!

BUT... BUT, KAI!

I'LL BE LOOKING FORWARD TO OUR NEXT BATTLE... YOU CAN *COUNT* ON IT!

TYSON! I'VE FOUND A WORTHY OPPONENT AT LONG LAST!

CAN'T YOU TELL WHAT I'M DOING!? I'M MAKING A *NEW* BEYBLADE...

WHAT ARE YOU UP TO?

AHHH! HI, CHIEF!

YOU SAW THAT?

I'LL SHOW HIM NOT TO MESS WITH MY THINGS!

...AND I'M GONNA *BEAT KAI* WITH IT!

snf!

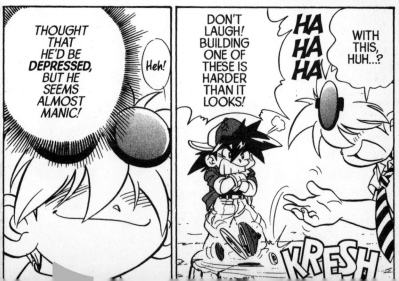

THOUGHT THAT HE'D BE DEPRESSED, BUT HE SEEMS ALMOST MANIC!

Heh!

DON'T LAUGH! BUILDING ONE OF THESE IS HARDER THAN IT LOOKS!

HA HA HA

WITH THIS, HUH...?

KRESH

WHEN I WAS LITTLE I HATED SWORD PLAY...

...SO I'D RUN AWAY FROM GRAMPS AND COME HERE TO PLAY WITH MY BEYBLADES.

I THINK I CAN UNDERSTAND HOW YOU FELT...

HITOSHI TAUGHT ME A WHOLE BUNCH OF THINGS...

...LIKE THE *BEST* WAY TO SPIN A BEYBLADE!

I GET IT! SO THAT'S WHEN YOUR TECHNIQUE FIRST TOOK ROOT!

EVEN MORE THAN JUST THAT!

IS IT SOME KIND OF BURIED TREASURE!?

IT'S RIGHT UNDER HERE!

COME TAKE A LOOK!

DRF

DRF

DRF

SPFF

LOOKS PRETTY OLD. CAN YOU STILL USE IT!?

HE'S BEEN HIDING IT FROM GRAMPS ALL THIS TIME!

IT'S A BEYBLADE THAT HITOSHI MADE!

K LIN K

TN K

IT'LL WORK FINE... *AFTER* I ADD THESE NEW PARTS!

READY TO GO! CHECK IT OUT!

HMMM! IT LOOKS COOL NOW!

AND NOW THOSE POWERS HAVE BEEN PASSED INTO FOUR BEYBLADES!

THE BLUE DRAGON FROM THE EAST

THOSE LIGHTS WERE THE FOUR BEASTS THAT WIELDED SACRED POWER.

THE CHIMERA FROM THE NORTH

THE PHOENIX FROM THE SOUTH

THE WHITE TIGER FROM THE WEST

YOU MEAN THE DRAGOON HAS BLUE DRAGON'S POWER!?

SO THE *PHOENIX* MUST BE...

...WHEN THE FOUR BEYBLADES OF LEGEND BECOME *ONE*...

AN OLD SAYING TELLS OF A DAY...

...KAI'S BEYBLADE DRANZER!

THAT'S WHAT KAI PLANS TO DO!

...AND INFINITE POWER WILL BE GAINED!

I'LL NEED MORE DATA ON THIS!

LEGENDARY POWER! TYSON, I-IT'S *AMAZING!*

COULD SUCH A THING REALLY BE *TRUE!?*

IT'S TOO *LATE!* THE DRAGOON IS NO MORE!

SURE, IT'S A COOL STORY... BUT WHAT DOES IT MATTER?

KWSH

JUST LIKE MY BIG BROTHER HITOSHI! BUT JIN CAN DO IT, TOO!?

BOTH AT ONE TIME!

BNGG

BNGG

TUMP

WHERE ARE YOU!? COME OUT!

HEY! HE'S GONE!

KaTNK

THAT'S THE RAGOON'S BIT!

FWUD

WHOA!

ALL IS NOT LOST!

YOUR NEW BEYBLADE? WHY PUT IT ON *THERE*?

tink knk

BUT WILL IT GO?

...SO, UNTIL I KNOW WHAT'S GOING ON...

JIN SAID THAT THE DRAGOON RESIDES IN *ME*...

...I'LL JUST KEEP HITTING THESE GONGS!

BUT HE WON'T QUIT!

HE STILL DOESN'T HAVE ENOUGH POWER!

DARN IT! JUST *ONE!*

BNGG

BNGG

YOUR HAND'S SWOLLEN! TYSON, THAT'S ENOUGH...

OW!

THRRB

NOT YET! I HAVE TO KEEP IT UP 'TIL I CAN HIT BOTH GONGS!

IT'S NO USE.

I...I CAN'T DO IT!

uff

hff

BNGG

WHAT GOOD WILL *THAT* DO!?

...PUT **ALL** YOUR FEELING INTO THE BEYBLADE! GIVE IT A TRY...

IT'S NOT LIKE YOU TO GIVE UP, TYSON! LISTEN TO ME...

HITOSHI!?

THE *FEELINGS* OF EACH BEYBLADER ARE THE KEY TO EVERY BATTLE!

GIVE THE BEYBLADE WHAT **YOU** FEEL! BOOST IT UP WITH **YOUR** WILL!

THE BLADE IS A **PART** OF YOU.

NOW WE KNOW THE SECRET OF THE BLUE DRAGON!

THE *REAL* DRAGOON IS THE *SPIRIT* THAT LIVES INSIDE THE *BIT!*

AMAZING, TYSON! I CAN HARDLY BELIEVE IT!

SEE THAT, CHIEF? BOTH GONGS WERE BLOWN APART!

174

THIS IS NO TIME TO *RACE!*

GRRRRR!

TSH TSH TSH

PAST THAT POINT, THE DOG'S...

...A *GONER!* THE CURRENT WILL TAKE HIM FOR SURE!

WOOM

I CAN'T CATCH UP TO HIM!

uff

hff

SPLRSH

Ween!

NOW *THAT'S* POWER FOR YOU! BUT...

IT'S SPINNIN ACROS THE WATER.

ZSH

ZSH

...THE CURRENT MADE IT MISS ITS MARK!

WSH

WM

NMSH

<NEVER GIVE UP!>

HUH!?

THEN IT'S NO USE!

tsh

...IT WOULD MAKE HIM A BEYBLADER OF *AMAZING* SKILL!

...TO DEFLECT TYSON'S DRAGOON AND HIT THE LOG...

IF HE PLANNED AHEAD OF TIME...

I'M SO GLAD YOU'RE OKAY!

arf arf

TEE, HEE!

slp

slp

WHAT? YOU CAN SPEAK JAPANESE!?

I HAD ONE AT MY HOUSE BACK IN AMERICA!

YUP, I SURE LOVE DOGS!

TOO BAD WE CAN'T TALK TO HIM!

HE'S A REAL DOG LOVER!

OH... I GET IT!

NO! THAT'S *MY* NAME!

HA HA!

HUH? YOU MEAN YOU KNOW THE DOG'S NAME?

THE NAME IS *MAX!*

SURE THING! PERFECT PLACE TO CLEAN OUT YOUR WET BEYBLADE!

WHOA! YOU MEAN YOUR HOUSE IS A *HOBBY SHOP!?*

PLASTIC MODELS

BEYBLADES

DAD!

HEY, *MAX!* WHERE YA BEEN?

I'M HOME, DADDY! WHERE ARE YOU?

HOW RAD!

WMP WMP WMP

YOU MEAN... *THAT'S* MAX'S *DAD!?*

Huh!?

BEYBLADE EXTREME ROTATION SHOOT VOL.1 END
CONTINUED IN VOL. 2

EDITOR'S RECOMMENDATIONS

MEGAMAN: by Ryo Takahashi. Our hero, Lan Hikari, synchronizes with *MEGAMAN* and becomes a super-charged dynamo. In and outside of the computer world they do their best to thwart the evil organization, World Three, from taking over the world.

THE BIG O: created by Hajime Yatate with story and art by Hitoshi Ariga a more than a straight adaptation of the hit Cartoon Network series, the manga includes the prequel to events in *THE BIG O* anime, plus many completely new stories.

ZOIDS: *CHAOTIC CENTURY* by Michiro Ueyama. Together, boy and machine fight for peace on Planet Zi. The anime was great. You'll love this series from VIZ, as well.

COMPLETE OUR SURVEY AND LET US KNOW WHAT YOU THINK!

☐ Please do NOT send me information about VIZ products, news and events, special offers, or other informatio

☐ Please do NOT send me information from VIZ's trusted business partners.

Name: _____

Address: _____

City: _____ **State:** _____ **Zip:** _____

E-mail: _____

☐ Male ☐ Female **Date of Birth** (mm/dd/yyyy): ___ / ___ / _____ (Under 13? Parental consent required

What race/ethnicity do you consider yourself? (please check one)

☐ Asian/Pacific Islander   ☐ Black/African American   ☐ Hispanic/Latino

☐ Native American/Alaskan Native   ☐ White/Caucasian   ☐ Other: _____

What VIZ product did you purchase? (check all that apply and indicate title purchased)

☐ DVD/VHS _____

☐ Graphic Novel _____

☐ Magazines _____

☐ Merchandise _____

Reason for purchase: (check all that apply)

☐ Special offer   ☐ Favorite title   ☐ Gift

☐ Recommendation   ☐ Other _____

Where did you make your purchase? (please check one)

☐ Comic store   ☐ Bookstore   ☐ Mass/Grocery Store

☐ Newsstand   ☐ Video/Video Game Store   ☐ Other: _____

☐ Online (site: _____)

What other VIZ properties have you purchased/own? _____

_____

How many anime and/or manga titles have you purchased in the last year? How many were VIZ titles? (please check one from each column)

ANIME	MANGA	VIZ
☐ None	☐ None	☐ None
☐ 1-4	☐ 1-4	☐ 1-4
☐ 5-10	☐ 5-10	☐ 5-10
☐ 11+	☐ 11+	☐ 11+

I find the pricing of VIZ products to be: (please check one)

☐ Cheap   ☐ Reasonable   ☐ Expensive

What genre of manga and anime would you like to see from VIZ? (please check two)

☐ Adventure   ☐ Comic Strip   ☐ Science Fiction   ☐ Fighting

☐ Horror   ☐ Romance   ☐ Fantasy   ☐ Sports

What do you think of VIZ's new look?

☐ Love It   ☐ It's OK   ☐ Hate It   ☐ Didn't Notice   ☐ No Opinion

Which do you prefer? (please check one)

☐ Reading right-to-left

☐ Reading left-to-right

Which do you prefer? (please check one)

☐ Sound effects in English

☐ Sound effects in Japanese with English captions

☐ Sound effects in Japanese only with a glossary at the back

THANK YOU! Please send the completed form to:

VIZ Survey
42 Catharine St.
Poughkeepsie, NY 12601